THE NEW BOOK OF

MUSCLES

Ian McChesney

CORPUS PUBLISHING

Dedication

To Eddie Caldwell for getting the ball rolling and to Nick Kent and Corpus Publishing for the opportunity to put this work into print. Also my thanks to Beryl Harper for her encouragement, help and advice at various stages of the project. Special thanks to Linda for putting up with my absences from everyday life and for tolerating the 'lost weekends'.

Ian McChesney, 2004

© Corpus Publishing Limited 2004

First published in 2004 by
Corpus Publishing Limited
PO Box 8, Lydney, Gloucestershire, United Kingdom GL15 6YD

Disclaimer

This publication is intended as an informational guide only. While the information contained herein is supplied in good faith, no responsibility is taken by the publisher or the author for any damage, injury or loss, however caused, which may arise from the use of the information provided.

British Library Cataloguing in Publication Data
A CIP record for this book is available from the British Library
ISBN 1 903333 17 2

Text and Cover Design: Sara Howell
Graphics: Amanda Williams
Printed and bound through Printworks International Ltd

Contents

Introduction

The idea for a book of this type first crossed my mind in about 1984 when I had been teaching anatomy and physiology to students studying for qualifications in hairdressing and beauty therapy for about seven years. In those days the students were required to learn about muscles in great detail and I had amassed a very comprehensive set of lecture notes and associated handouts.

In the course of my work I had produced lots of learning materials in booklet form and often thought it would be a good idea to write a book that would be of use to similar students elsewhere. However, with a young family, improvements to the house, a fairly heavy teaching load and other distractions I never actually got round to it.

Then, in 2002 Eddie Caldwell (Principal of the Northern Institute of Massage) put me in touch with Nick Kent of Corpus Publishing and after some discussion, I was asked to write this book.

I have attempted to make the book of interest to as wide a range of students as possible. Basic facts and diagrams are provided for many of the major muscles of the body and students of hairdressing and beauty therapy who are studying anatomy and physiology will find it fulfils their needs. Those involved in complementary therapies, sports studies, dance and/or exercise will also find the book very helpful.

By including more detail (usually in italics) I envisage that the book will also appeal to those studying massage therapy and similar courses and that the additional information will provide extra detail needed by students on physiotherapy and related advanced level courses.

I have assumed some basic knowledge of anatomical structures and terminology but, for the absolute beginner, a diagram of the relevant parts of the skeleton to which they are attached accompanies most muscles. There is also a list of basic anatomical definitions prior to the main section of the book. Some basic terminology is explained and I have included a section that deals with the naming of muscles.

Most pages have a similar format where essential information regarding positions, origins, insertions and actions accompany diagrams of the muscles and the skeleton. More detailed notes on nerve and blood supplies are also provided for those that need them. With reference to the nerve supplies, it should be noted that various authorities supply different information. This is largely due to the difficulty in tracing the paths of the spinal nerves during dissection. In this book, I have used a combination of the information supplied by Romanes, and Williamson and Warwick (see page 64).

Information is included on synergists and antagonists for each muscle and possible weaknesses are outlined as pointers towards diagnosis for the massage therapist. Finally, some additional notes are included by way of amplification and clarification. The amount of detail here varies quite considerably from one muscle to another.

How to use this book

For ease of use the muscles are listed in alphabetical order and except for a few exceptions, the pages have the same format as below. The book describes the positions, origins, insertions and actions of many of the major muscles of the body. In addition, diagrams of the muscles and the bones of the skeleton to which they are attached are provided. There is information relevant to the diagnosis of muscle weaknesses and additional information is included for the more advanced student.

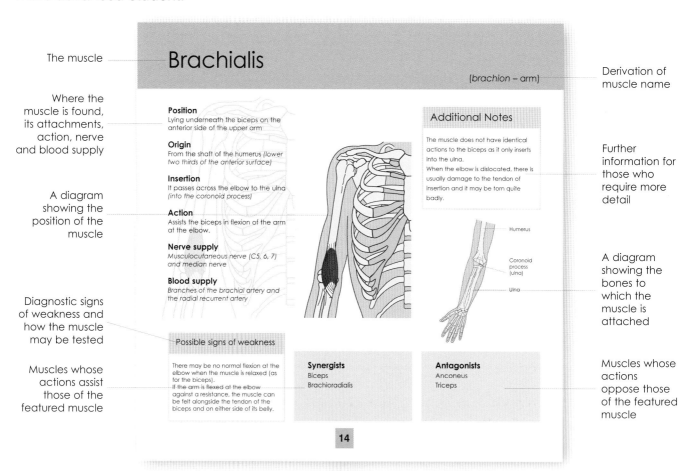

The muscle

Brachialis

(brachion – arm)

Derivation of muscle name

Where the muscle is found, its attachments, action, nerve and blood supply

Position
Lying underneath the biceps on the anterior side of the upper arm

Origin
From the shaft of the humerus (lower two thirds of the anterior surface)

Insertion
It passes across the elbow to the ulna (into the coronoid process)

Action
Assists the biceps in flexion of the arm at the elbow.

Nerve supply
Musculocutaneous nerve (C5, 6, 7) and median nerve

Blood supply
Branches of the brachial artery and the radial recurrent artery

A diagram showing the position of the muscle

Additional Notes

The muscle does not have identical actions to the biceps as it only inserts into the ulna.
When the elbow is dislocated, there is usually damage to the tendon of insertion and it may be torn quite badly.

Further information for those who require more detail

Humerus

Coronoid process (ulna)

Ulna

A diagram showing the bones to which the muscle is attached

Diagnostic signs of weakness and how the muscle may be tested

Possible signs of weakness

There may be no normal flexion at the elbow when the muscle is relaxed (as for the biceps).
If the arm is flexed at the elbow against a resistance, the muscle can be felt alongside the tendon of the biceps and on either side of its belly.

Muscles whose actions assist those of the featured muscle

Synergists
Biceps
Brachioradialis

Antagonists
Anconeus
Triceps

Muscles whose actions oppose those of the featured muscle

14

Terminology

Understanding anatomical terminology can be a very daunting experience for students but unfortunately it cannot be avoided. As you read through this book you will find some terms that are fairly complicated and many of these are explained as they arise.

However, it is essential that the student is aware of certain definitions before looking at the muscles featured in this book. These are listed below.

Superior   Above, the upper surface or towards the upper part of the body

Inferior   Below, the lower surface or towards the lower part of the body

Anterior   The front surface, in front of or towards the front of the body

Posterior   The rear surface, behind or towards the rear of the body

Medial   Near or nearest to the mid-line of the body

Lateral   Away from or furthest from the mid-line of the body

Proximal   Nearest to the point of attachment

Distal   Furthest from the point of attachment

External   Outside or outer surface

Internal   Inside or inner surface

Origin   The fixed end of a muscle (usually nearest the mid-line)

Insertion   The attachment of a muscle where movement occurs (usually furthest away from the mid-line)

Abduction	Movement away from the mid-line of the body
Adduction	Movement towards the mid-line of the body
Extension	Increases the angle at a joint; straightening at a joint
Flexion	Decreases the angle at a joint; bending at a joint
Eversion	Turning the sole of the foot outwards
Inversion	Turning the sole of the foot inwards
Dorsiflexion	Flexion of the foot at the ankle
Plantar flexion	Extension of the foot at the ankle
Depressor	Produces a downward movement
Levator	Produces an upward movement
Pronation	Turning the palm of the hand downward
Supination	Turning the palm of the hand upward
Rotation	Moving a bone around its long axis
Circumduction	Moving a limb to describe a cone shape in the air
Prime mover	The main muscle involved in a particular action (may also be called *agonists*)
Synergists	Muscles on the same side of a joint that have similar actions
Antagonists	Muscles that have opposite actions at a joint
Fixators	Muscles that stabilise joints giving prime movers a rigid base from which to work

Muscle tissue

Muscle cells have the ability to shorten their length and thicken in width by contracting. In order to contract, muscles must be excitable (able to respond to stimuli from nerve impulses). After contracting, their elasticity enables them to return to their original shape. They also have properties of extensibility whereby they can be stretched.

There are three types of muscle tissue in the body as follows:

Cardiac muscle tissue composes most of the vertebrate heart. The cells, which have longitudinal and cross striations, each possess a single nucleus and form a branched network of interlinked fibres. Cardiac muscle is not under voluntary control and a small patch of nervous tissue in the heart wall controls its rate of contraction. This is commonly known as the pacemaker and it is supplied with nerves from the autonomic nervous system, which can override the pacemaker and alter its rate of contraction during exercise. It contracts at about seventy times per minute at rest, pumping about 5 litres of blood each minute.

Smooth muscle (also known as **visceral**, or **involuntary**, muscle) is composed of spindle-shaped cells, each having a central nucleus with longitudinal striations in their cytoplasm. Stimuli for the contractions of smooth muscles are delivered by the autonomic nervous system. Smooth muscle is found in the skin, inside many internal organs, in structures of the reproductive system, in the walls of major blood vessels, and in parts of the excretory system. The contraction of smooth muscle is generally not under voluntary control.

It can:
• Regulate the flow of blood in the arteries
• Move food through the gastrointestinal tract
• Expel urine from the bladder.

Skeletal muscle tissue is usually attached to bones of the skeleton and is the type of muscle with which this book deals. It is **striated** (striped) and **voluntary** (under conscious control). As its name implies, it is the muscle that moves bones of the skeleton. This type of muscle is composed of

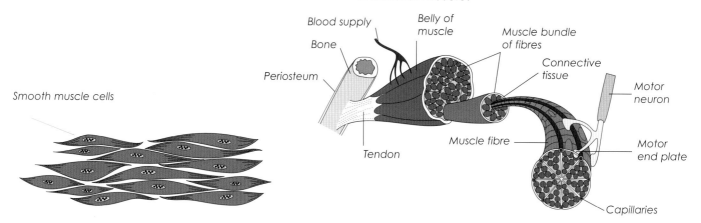

Muscle cells and the muscle fibre of a skeletal muscle.

Smooth muscle cells

Blood supply

Bone

Periosteum

Belly of muscle

Muscle bundle of fibres

Connective tissue

Motor neuron

Tendon

Muscle fibre

Motor end plate

Capillaries

long fibres surrounded by a sheath called the **sarcolemma**. The fibres are elongated, cylindrical cells containing many nuclei with longitudinal and cross striations in the cytoplasm. Skeletal muscle is supplied with impulses by nerves from the central nervous system. Most skeletal muscles are connected to bones of the skeleton by tough attachments called tendons.

Skeletal muscles can account for almost half of our body weight and give us the ability to move around. They consist of fibres that can contract when they receive nervous impulses from the brain. The muscles are attached to bones by tendons and when a muscle contracts, it pulls on a tendon which in turn pulls on a bone and causes movement.

A single skeletal muscle, such as the triceps muscle, is attached at its **origin** to the humerus (which does not move) and at its **insertion**, to the ulna where movement occurs. Skeletal muscles can only produce movement when they contract, not when they relax. In other words a muscle may pull but it cannot push. For this reason most muscles are arranged in pairs which have opposite actions.

As the triceps contracts, the insertion is pulled toward the origin and the arm is straightened or extended at the elbow. Thus the triceps is an extensor. Because skeletal muscle exerts force only when it contracts, a second muscle, a flexor, is needed to flex or bend the joint. The biceps muscle is the flexor of the lower arm. Together, the biceps and triceps make up an **antagonistic** pair of muscles. Similar pairs, working antagonistically across other joints, provide almost all the movements of the skeleton.

Adductors of the thigh
(a group of four muscles on the medial aspect of the thigh)

Position
A group of four muscles covering the medial thigh

Origin
From the ischium and pubis (see additional notes, right)

Insertion
Into the femur *(linea aspera)*

Action
Adduction and lateral rotation of the thigh

Nerve supply
Obdurator (L2, 3, 4) and femoral (L3, 4) nerves

Blood supply
Lateral femoral circumflex, medial femoral circumflex, branches of profunda femoris and saphenous branch of descending genicular arteries

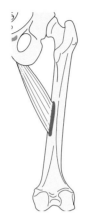

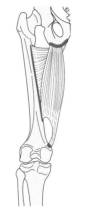

Adductor longus   Adductor magnus

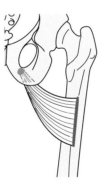

Pectineus

Adductor brevis

Additional Notes

The group consists of the *adductor longus, adductor brevis, adductor magnus* and *pectineus (adductor* – moves towards midline; *longus* – long; *brevis* – short; *magnus* – large; *pectineus* – comb shaped). *Pecten* (a comb) is the old name for the pubis. The muscles can adduct the thigh and continue the action to cross one thigh over the other. They are used in horse riding to grip the saddle. The pectineus and adductor longus are thought to be involved in flexion of the thigh. The muscles are innervated by the obdurator nerve except the pectineus, which is supplied by the femoral nerve. They all originate from the pubis, but the adductor magnus also has an origin from the ischium. Their insertions run the length of the femur along the linea aspera.

Possible signs of weakness

'Bow legs' and a lateral sway when standing. Difficulty in locking the knees together.
If the patient lies on his/her back and extends the knee against a resistance, the muscles can easily be felt.

Synergists
Gracilis
Other adductors

Antagonists
Gluteus medius
Psoas
Sartorius

Anconeus

Position
A short muscle running from the humerus to the ulna

Origin
From the distal end of the humerus *(posterior side of the lateral epicondyle)*

Insertion
Into the proximal end of the ulna *(olecranon process and upper part of the posterior aspect of the shaft)*

Action
Extension of the forearm at the elbow

Nerve supply
Radial nerve (C7, 8)

Blood supply
Middle collateral artery

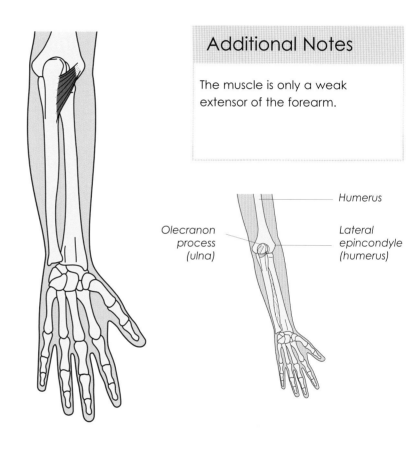

Humerus

Olecranon process (ulna)

Lateral epincondyle (humerus)

Additional Notes

The muscle is only a weak extensor of the forearm.

Possible signs of weakness

Flexion of the elbow when the arm is held at the side.

Synergists
Pronator teres
Triceps

Antagonists
Biceps
Brachioradialis

Biceps brachii

(biceps – two heads of origin; *brachion* – arm)

Position
A large muscle on the anterior surface of the upper arm

Origin
By two tendons from scapula (see additional notes, right)

Insertion
Into the head of the radius *(radial tuberosity)*

Action
Flexes the arm at the elbow, stabilises the shoulder joint and supinates the palm of the hand

Nerve supply
Musculocutaneous nerve (C5, 6, 7)

Blood supply
Branches of the brachial artery

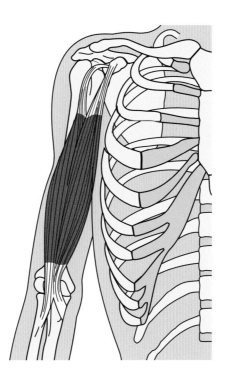

Additional Notes

The shorter head of the muscle originates from the coracoid process of the scapula while the longer head originates from the rim of the glenoid cavity and its tendon runs along the biciptal groove of the humerus. The insertion into the radius is on the medial side and this allows the radius to rotate, to supinate the hand. This is of use when undoing a stiff top on a jar or removing the cork from a wine bottle. There is also an insertion into the fascia that covers the pronator teres.

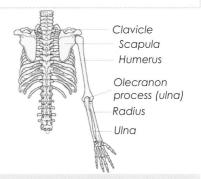

Clavicle
Scapula
Humerus
Olecranon process (ulna)
Radius
Ulna

Possible signs of weakness

There is usually slight flexion at the elbow when standing with the muscle relaxed. When weak, this may not occur and the arm will be held straight.
The muscle can be examined when the patient flexes the supinated forearm against a resistance with the arm held at the side of the body.

Synergists
Brachialis
Brachioradialis

Antagonists
Anconeus
Pronator teres
Triceps

Brachialis

Position
Lying underneath the biceps on the anterior side of the upper arm

Origin
From the shaft of the humerus *(lower two thirds of the anterior surface)*

Insertion
It passes across the elbow to the ulna *(into the coronoid process)*

Action
Assists the biceps in flexion of the arm at the elbow.

Nerve supply
Musculocutaneous nerve (C5, 6, 7) and median nerve

Blood supply
Branches of the brachial artery and the radial recurrent artery

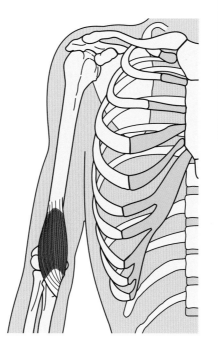

Additional Notes

The muscle does not have identical actions to the biceps as it only inserts into the ulna.
When the elbow is dislocated, there is usually damage to the tendon of insertion and it may be torn quite badly.

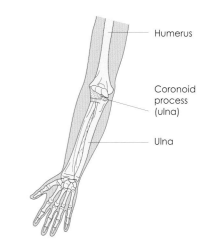

Humerus

Coronoid process (ulna)

Ulna

Possible signs of weakness

There may be no normal flexion at the elbow when the muscle is relaxed (as for the biceps).
If the arm is flexed at the elbow against a resistance, the muscle can be felt alongside the tendon of the biceps and on either side of its belly.

Synergists
Biceps
Brachioradialis

Antagonists
Anconeus
Triceps

Brachioradialis

(brachion – arm; *radialis* – radius)*

Position
Lies on the lateral surface of the humerus

Origin
From the lateral side of humerus near the elbow *(from the supracondylar ridge just above the lateral epicondyle)*

Insertion
Into the head of the radius *(just above the styloid process)*

Action
Helps to flex the arm at the elbow *(it also aids in rotation of the forearm)*

Nerve supply
Radial nerve (C5, 6)

Blood supply
Radial recurrent artery

Possible signs of weakness

There may be no normal flexion at the elbow when the muscle is relaxed (as for the biceps).
If the forearm is bent at right angles midway between pronation and supination, the muscle can be seen and felt if the arm is flexed at the elbow against a resistance.

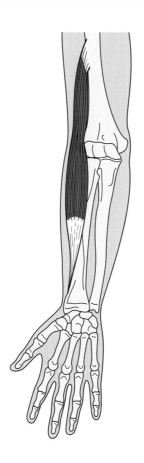

Additional Notes

Although it originates close to the lateral epincondyle of the humerus, it is involved in flexion at the elbow. Other muscles that originate from this area tend to be extensors of the arm at the elbow.
It lies superficially on the lateral side of the humerus, but its tendon of insertion is covered by those of the adductor pollicis longus and the extensor pollicis brevis.

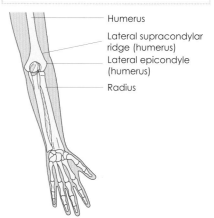

Humerus

Lateral supracondylar ridge (humerus)

Lateral epicondyle (humerus)

Radius

Synergists
Biceps
Brachialis

Antagonists
Anconeus
Triceps

Coracobrachialis

(coraco – coracoid process; brachion – arm)

Position
It runs between the scapula and the humerus

Origin
From the scapula *(coracoid process)*

Insertion
Into the humerus half-way down the medial side

Action
Flexes and adducts arm

Nerve supply
Musculocutaneous nerve (C5, 6, 7)

Blood supply
Branches of the brachial artery

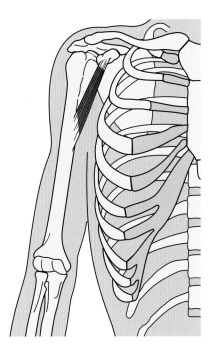

Additional Notes

It is the equivalent of the adductor muscles of the hip.

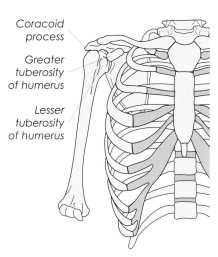

Coracoid process

Greater tuberosity of humerus

Lesser tuberosity of humerus

Possible signs of weakness

There may be noticeable fatigue during actions such as eating or washing or brushing hair.

Synergists
Biceps
Deltoid
Pectoralis major

Antagonists
Deltoid
Latissimus dorsi
Teres major
Teres minor

Deltoid

(delta – a triangle)

Position
A triangular muscle covering the shoulder

Origin
From the clavicle *(outer third of the anterior surface)* and the scapula *(outer border of the acromion process and lower border of the spine of the scapula)*

Insertion
Into the humerus *(the deltoid tuberosity almost half-way down its lateral side)*

Action
It abducts the humerus *(it is also involved in rotation of the arm at the shoulder and helps to stabilise the shoulder joint*

Nerve supply
Axillary nerve (C5, 6)

Blood supply
Posterior humeral circumflex artery and deltoid branch of the thoracoacromial artery

Possible signs of weakness

Difficulty in holding the arm out to the side. The palm may turn forwards or backwards when standing with the arms at the side.
If the arm is abducted to 45 degrees in the plane of the scapula and then held there against a resistance, the muscle can be easily seen and felt.

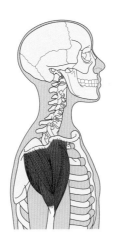

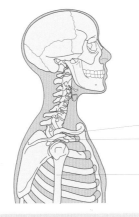

Acromion process
Spine of scapula

Humerus

Additional Notes

The muscle is divided into anterior, lateral and posterior parts, each having separate origins (see left). All three parts converge into a common insertion.
The anterior part of the muscle is more rounded and pronounced than the posterior part. If the shoulder is dislocated, the roundness of the front part of the muscle is lost.
The anterior fibres move the arm forwards and help in medial rotation. The lateral fibres abduct the arm. The posterior fibres move the arms backwards and help in lateral rotation.

Synergists
Supraspinatus
Teres major
Pectoralis major

Antagonists
Coracobrachialis
Latissimus dorsi
Teres major
Teres minor

Erector spinae

(erector – erect; *spinae* – of the spine)*

Position
Three complex groups of overlapping muscles lying in the grooves on each side of the backbone

Origin
From various points up the length of the backbone (see additional notes, right)

Insertion
Into various points up the length of the backbone (see additional notes, right)

Action
Bilateral: maintain the lumbar and cervical curves, maintain an upright position, extend the head and vertebral column
Unilateral: lateral flexion of the spine and rotation to same side

Nerve supply
Dorsal rami of cervical, thoracic and lumbar nerves

Blood supply
Branches of the aorta

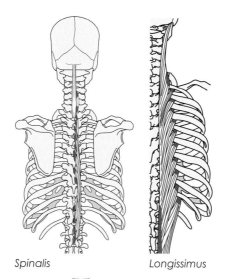

Spinalis   Longissimus

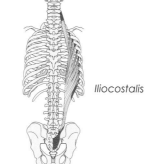

Iliocostalis

Additional Notes

The erector spinae run along each side of the backbone with attachments from the pelvis to the head and are also known as the *sacrospinalis* muscles. They arise from a broad, thick tendon that is attached to the sacrum, ilium and some of the lumbar and thoracic vertebrae. From here, three main muscles run up each side of the spine as follows:

- a lateral *iliocostalis* group (*ilio* – flank; *costa* – rib) running from the iliac crest as far as the cervical vertebrae
- an intermediate *longissimus* group (*longissimus* – longest) running from the ilium as far as the temporal bone
- a medial *spinalis* group (*spinalis* – of the spine) running from the lumbar and thoracic vertebrae to the occipital bone.

Each of these muscles is subdivided into three parts, and, in all cases, there is overlapping of the origins and insertions.

For more detailed information, see Bibliography (page 64).

Possible signs of weakness

The spine may rotate towards the weaker side. Bilateral weakness can cause kyphosis.

Synergists
Extensors of the back
Quadratus lumborum

Antagonists
Abdominal muscles
Opposite erector spinae

Extensors of the foot
(*extensor* – increases the angle at a joint/straightening at a joint)

Position
A pair of muscles on the anterior surface of the lower leg

Origin
From the tibia and fibula (see additional notes, right)

Insertion
Into the superior surface of the phalanges of the toes (see additional notes, right)

Action
Extension of the toes and dorsiflexion of the foot (see additional notes, right)

Nerve supply
Deep peroneal nerve (L4, 5; S1)

Blood supply
Anterior tibial artery

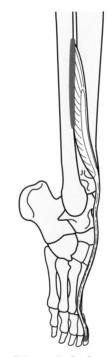

Extensor hallucis longus

Extensor digitorum longus

Additional Notes

The extensor digitorum longus (*extensor* – increases the angle at a joint straightens at a joint; *digitorum* – finger or toe) originates from the upper three quarters of the anterior surface of the fibula and the lateral condyle of the tibia. Its tendon of insertion passes in front of the ankle joint and inserts into the middle and distal phalanges of toes 2, 3, 4, and 5.
The extensor hallucis longus (*hallucis* – of the big toe) originates from the middle of the anterior surface of the tibia and inserts into the distal phalanx of the big toe (*hallux*). Its tendon is very pronounced when the big toe is extended.
Both muscles contribute to dorsiflexion of the foot.

Possible signs of weakness

Difficulty in extending the toes and possible collapse of medial longitudinal arch.
The tendons are prominent if the toes are extended against a resistance.

Synergists
Tibialis anterior
Peroneus tertius

Antagonists
Flexor digitorum longus
Flexor hallucis longus
Gastrocnemius
Soleus
Tibialis posterior

Extensors of the wrist

(*extensor* – increases the angle at a joint/straightening at a joint)

Position
A group of three muscles on the posterior forearm

Origin
From the distal end of the humerus (*lateral epicondyle*)

Insertion
Into the metacarpals and phalanges (see additional notes, right)

Action
Extension, abduction and adduction of the wrist. Extension of the phalanges (see additional notes, right)

Nerve supply
Posterior interosseous nerve (C6, 7, 8) – a branch of the radial nerve

Blood supply
Radial recurrent and posterior interosseous arteries

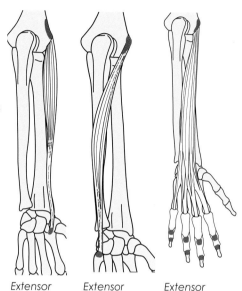

Extensor carpi radius longus

Extensor carpi ulnaris

Extensor digitorum

Possible signs of weakness

The wrist and/or fingers will be flexed when relaxed. If the extended fingers are flexed at their base against a resistance, the extensor digitorum can be felt. If the fingers are extended and the wrist is extended against a resistance towards the radius or ulna, the tendons of the other two muscles are clearly seen.

Additional Notes

This group of muscles consists of the *extensor carpi radialis longus, extensor carpi ulnaris* and *extensor digitorum* (*carpi* – of the carpals; *radialis* – of the radius; *ulnaris* – of the ulna; *digitorum* – of the fingers or toes; *longus* – long). They have a common origin, but their action is determined by their insertions:

- The *extensor carpi radialis* inserts into the second metacarpal and extends and abducts the wrist;
- The *extensor carpi ulnaris* inserts into the fifth metacarpal and extends and adducts the wrist;
- The *extensor digitorum* inserts into the middle and distal phalanges of the fingers and extends the fingers.

The *extensor digitorum longus* is supplied by the radial recurrent artery while the other two muscles are supplied by the posterior interosseous artery.

Synergists
The muscles are synergists to each other

Antagonists
Flexor carpi radialis
Flexor carpi ulnaris
Palmaris longus

External obliques

Position
They lie under the rectus abdominis and run around the sides of the abdomen

Origin
As eight strips from lower eight ribs

Insertion
Into the iliac crest *(pubic tubercle)* and linea alba

Action
Compression of the abdomen (see additional notes, right). Contraction of one side causes lateral flexion of the vertebral column

Nerve supply
Thoracic nerves (T6-12) and iliohypogastric nerve

Blood supply
Intercostal, subcostal, superior and inferior epigastric arteries

Additional Notes

The fibres of the muscle run downward and medially and the digitations of the origin merge with those of the serratus anterior. The linea alba is an aponeurosis formed by the fibres of the left and right abdominal muscles. The *umbilicus* is the scar that is left after sectioning of the umbilical cord at birth. The *lumbar fascia* provides attachment for several other muscles in this area. Contraction is also apparent during defecation, vomiting, urination and childbirth.

Abdominal aponeurosis

Anterior iliac crest

Possible signs of weakness

The shoulder may rotate forwards. The trunk may lean towards the weaker side and if there is bilateral weakness, lordosis of the spine may occur.

Synergists
Internal obliques
Rectus abdominis

Antagonists
Gluteus medius
Gluteus minimus
Opposite obliques

Flexors of the foot

(flexor – decreases the angle at a joint/bending at a joint)

Position
A pair of muscles on the posterior surface of the lower leg

Origin
Tibia and fibula (see additional notes, right)

Insertion
The inferior surface of the distal phalanges of the toes (see additional notes, right)

Action
Flexion of the toes *(and support for the medial longitudinal arch when walking)*

Nerve supply
Tibial nerve (L5; S1, 2)

Blood supply
Peroneal and posterior tibial arteries

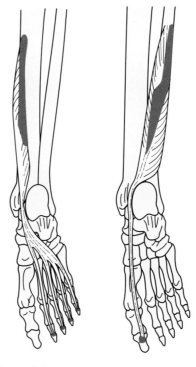

Flexor digitorum longus

Flexor hallucis longus

Note: The foot is plantar flexed.

Additional Notes

The flexor digitorum longus (*flexor –* decreases the angle at a joint/bends at a joint; *digitorum –* finger or toe; *longus –* long) originates from the upper posterior surface of the tibia on the medial side. It inserts via four divisions into the inferior surface of the distal phalanges of toes 2-5.
The flexor hallucis longus (*hallucis –* of the big toe) originates from the lower two-thirds of the posterior surface of the fibula and inserts into the inferior surface of the distal phalanx of the big toe *(hallux).*

Possible signs of weakness

Hyperextension of the toes and a tendency towards pronation of the foot.
If the patient tries to flex toes 2-5 at their base against a resistance, the bellies of the muscles can be felt.

Synergists
Gastrocnemius
Peroneal muscles
Soleus
Tibialis posterior

Antagonists
Extensor digitorum longus
Extensor hallucis longus
Tibialis anterior

Flexors of the wrist

(flexor – decreases the angle at a joint/bending at a joint)

Position
A group of three muscles on the anterior forearm

Origin
From the distal end of the humerus *(medial epicondyle)* and proximal end of the radius (see additional notes, right)

Insertion
Into the carpals, metacarpals and palmar aponeurosis (see additional notes, right)

Action
Abduction, adduction and flexion of the wrist

Nerve supply
Median (C6, 7) and ulnar (C8, T1) nerves

Blood supply
Branches of the ulnar and radial arteries

Flexor carpi radialis

Flexor carpi ulnaris

Palmaris longus

Additional Notes

This group of muscles consists of the *flexor carpi radialis, flexor carpi ulnaris,* and the *palmaris longus (flexor* – decreases the angle at a joint/bending at a joint; *carpi* – of the carpals; *radialis* – of the radius; *ulnaris* – of the ulna; *palmaris* – of the palm; *longus* – long). They all originate from the medial epicondyle of the humerus, but the flexor carpi ulnaris is also attached to the head of the radius. Their insertions are as follows:

• Flexor carpi radialis into the second and third metacarpals
• Flexor carpi ulnaris into the pisiform, hamate and fifth metacarpal
• Palmaris longus into the palmar aponeurosis

They all flex the wrist but the flexor carpi ulnaris is involved in adduction and the flexor carpi radialis in abduction. The flexor carpi ulnaris is supplied by the median nerve; the other muscles by the ulnar nerve. The flexor carpi radialis is supplied by the radial artery; the other muscles by the ulnar artery.

Possible signs of weakness

The wrist may be limp and extended. If the *dorsum* (posterior surface) of the forearm is placed flat on a table and the wrist is flexed against a resistance, the tendons of these muscles are easily seen.

Synergists
The muscles are synergists to each other

Antagonists
Extensor carpi radialis
Extensor carpi ulnaris

Gastrocnemius

(gaster – belly; *kneme* – leg)

Position
The main muscle of the calf

Origin
From both condyles of the femur
(medial and lateral)

Insertion
Into the heel bone *(calcaneus)* via
the Achilles tendon

Action
Provides propulsion in walking,
running and jumping. Plantar flexes
the foot and flexes the knee

Nerve supply
Tibial nerve (L5; S1, 2)

Blood supply
*Branches of the popliteal, peroneal
and posterior tibial arteries*

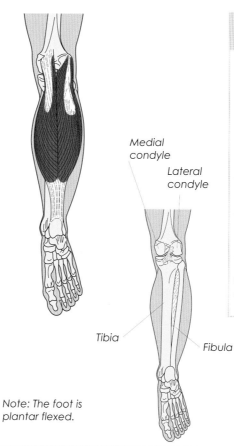

Medial
condyle

Lateral
condyle

Tibia

Fibula

Note: The foot is
plantar flexed.

Additional Notes

The Achilles tendon is also known as
the *tendo calcaneus* or *calcaneal
tendon.* Its common name arises from
Greek mythology, where Achilles was
immersed in the River Styx by his
mother so as to be immune in battle.
She held him by his heel, which
obviously was not dipped in water.
Achilles met his death in the Trojan
Wars, when he was fatally wounded
by a spear that penetrated his heel.
When the muscle is contracted while
standing, the subject will rise onto tip
toes.

Possible signs of weakness

The subject may have difficulty in
standing on tip toes.
If the patient lies in a prone position
and tries to plantar flex the foot
against a resistance, the belly of the
muscle is easily seen and felt.

Synergists
Flexor digitorum longus
Flexor hallucis longus
Peroneal muscles
Soleus
Tibialis posterior

Antagonists
Quadriceps
Tibialis anterior

Gluteus maximus

(glutos – buttock; maximus – largest)

Position
A large muscle forming the bulk of the buttocks

Origin
From the iliac crest, sacrum and coccyx

Insertion
Into the lateral side of the femur, just below its head *(the gluteal tuberosity)*

Action
Extends the flexed thigh and rotates the thigh laterally

Nerve supply
Inferior gluteal nerve (L5, S1, S2)

Blood supply
Inferior and superior gluteal arteries

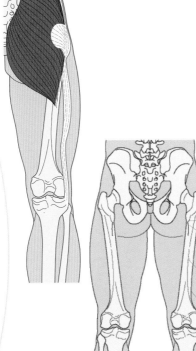

Greater trochanter (femur)

Lesser trochanter

Gluteal tuberosity (femur)

Linea aspera (femur)

Femur

Additional Notes

Some authorities claim that this is the strongest muscle in the body. When it contracts, a definite 'dimple' can be seen close to the greater trochanter of the femur. It is used in many everyday actions, such as standing up from a sitting position and walking up a slope.
The muscle also inserts into the *fascia lata*, which is a thick layer of fibrous tissue that surrounds the muscles of the thigh (at its lateral border, this fascia is thickened to form the *iliotibial tract*). The tensor fascia lata also inserts here and so the gluteus maximus is likely to have some action on the knee joint.

Possible signs of weakness

There may be difficulty in straightening the body when standing. Possible anterior rotation of the pelvis and/or medial rotation of the leg. Bow legs due to instability of the knee.
The muscle can be easily felt if the patient tries to lift the thigh off the couch when lying in a prone position.

Synergists
Biceps femoris
Hamstrings
Rectus femoris
Sartorius

Antagonists
Adductor muscles
Gluteus medius
Iliacus
Psoas

Gluteus medius

(glutos – buttock; *medius* – middle)*

Position
It lies underneath the gluteus maximus

Origin
From the posterior surface of the ilium

Insertion
Into the head of the femur *(greater trochanter)*

Action
Abduction and medial rotation of the thigh

Nerve supply
Superior gluteal nerve (L4, 5, S1)

Blood supply
Superior gluteal artery

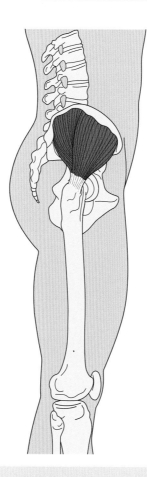

Additional Notes

The action of this muscle is vital when walking, as it shifts the centre of gravity over the foot that is in contact with the ground. This allows the other foot to be raised and moved forwards easily.

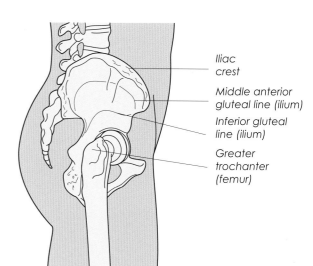

Iliac crest

Middle anterior gluteal line (ilium)

Inferior gluteal line (ilium)

Greater trochanter (femur)

Possible signs of weakness

There may be a lateral movement of the hips and possible twisting of the pelvis. The hip joint may be unstable and knock knees may be seen.
If the patient is lying on his/her back, the muscle can be felt when the thigh is abducted with the leg straight.

Synergists
Gluteus maximus
Gluteus minimus
Tensor fasciae latae

Antagonists
Adductor muscles
Gluteus maximus
Gracilis
Piriformis

Gluteus minimus

(*glutos* – buttock; *minimus* – smallest)

Position
It lies underneath the gluteus medius and is the smallest gluteal muscle

Origin
From the posterior surface of the ilium

Insertion
Into the head of the femur *(greater trochanter)*

Action
Abduction and lateral rotation of the thigh

Nerve supply
Superior gluteal nerve (L4, 5, S1)

Blood supply
Superior gluteal artery

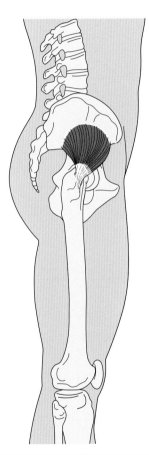

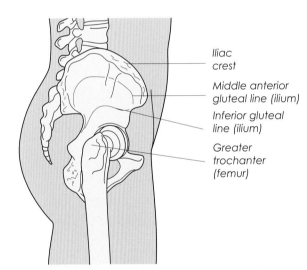

Iliac crest

Middle anterior gluteal line (ilium)

Inferior gluteal line (ilium)

Greater trochanter (femur)

Additional Notes

The gluteus minimus assists the gluteus medius during walking.

Possible signs of weakness

Similar to gluteus medius; the hips may shift or sway to the side.
If the patient is lying on his/her back, the muscle can be felt when the thigh is abducted with the leg straight.

Synergists
Gluteus maximus
Gluteus medius
Tensor fasciae latae

Antagonists
Adductor muscles
Gluteus maximus
Gracilis
Piriformis

Gracilis

Position
A slender muscle on the medial surface of the thigh

Origin
From the pubic bone (*symphysis pubis and pubic arch*)

Insertion
Into the medial side of the upper part of the tibia

Action
Adduction, medial rotation and flexion of the thigh

Nerve supply
Obturator nerve (L2, 3, 4)

Blood supply
Obturator artery

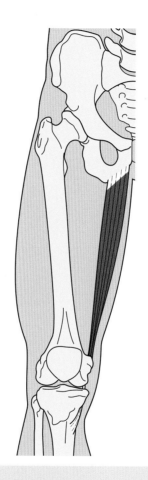

Possible signs of weakness
May cause knock knees or posterior rotation of the pelvis.

Additional Notes
It inserts very close to the sartorius and some authorities claim that it is also involved in flexion of the knee.

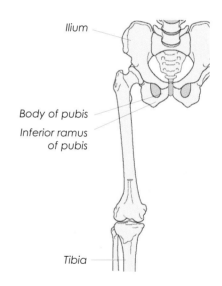

Ilium

Body of pubis

Inferior ramus of pubis

Tibia

Synergists
Adductor muscles
Hamstrings
Sartorius

Antagonists
Iliacus
Psoas
Quadriceps
Sartorius

Hamstrings

(a collective name for a group of three muscles)

Position
A group of three muscles on the posterior thigh

Origin
From the ischium and femur (see additional notes, right)

Insertion
Into the tibia and fibula (see additional notes, right)

Action
Flexion of the leg at the knee and extension of the thigh at the hip

Nerve supply
Tibial nerve (L5, S1, 2) from sciatic nerve

Blood supply
Branches of the profunda femoris artery and inferior gluteal artery

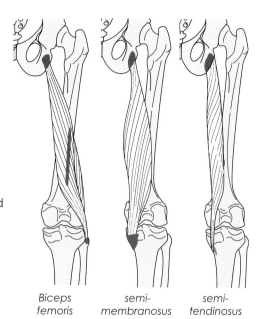

Biceps femoris   semi-membranosus   semi-tendinosus

Additional Notes

The group consists of the *biceps femoris, semitendinosus* and *semimembranosus (biceps* – two heads; *femoris* – of the femur; *semi* – half; *tendo* – tendon; *membran* – membrane).

All three muscles originate from the ischial tuberosity of the pelvis but the biceps femoris also has a short head of origin from the linea aspera of the femur. The biceps femoris inserts into the head of the fibula while its partners insert into the tibia (the semitendinosus into the medial surface of the upper shaft and the semimembranosus into the back of the medial condyle).

The muscles pass across two joints and this explains their dual action.

Some people have difficulty in touching their toes due to shortness of the hamstrings.

Possible signs of weakness

'Knock knees' if the weakness is medial; 'bow legs' if lateral. Bilateral weakness can cause anterior rotation of the pelvis. The tibia may rotate medially or laterally, depending upon which side is weak.
If the patient is lying face down, the tendons of the muscles are obvious when the leg is flexed at the knee against a resistance.

Synergists
Gastrocnemius
Gracilis
Sartorius

Antagonists
Iliacus
Psoas
Quadriceps femoris

Iliacus

Position
A triangular muscle inside the pelvis

Origin
From the anterior surface of the ilium
(*iliac fossa*)

Insertion
It merges with the tendon of the psoas, which inserts into the head of the femur (*lesser trochanter*)

Action
Flexion and lateral rotation of the thigh

Nerve supply
Femoral nerve (L2, 3)

Blood supply
Branches of the medial femoral circumflex artery

Additional Notes

Together with the psoas, it is the main flexor of the thigh.
The two muscles are often referred to as the *iliopsoas*.
When lying on the back, they are used to raise the body into a sitting position. To work just the abdominal muscles, sit-ups should not be performed to the vertical position.

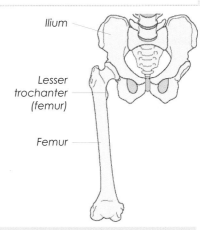

Ilium

Lesser trochanter (femur)

Femur

Possible signs of weakness

May cause posterior rotation of the pelvis.

Synergists
Adductor muscles
Psoas
Rectus femoris

Antagonists
Gluteus maximus
Gracilis
Hamstrings

Infraspinatus

Position
It runs from the scapula to the humerus

Origin
From just below the spine of the scapula *(infraspinous fossa)*

Insertion
Into the head of the humerus *(greater tubercle)*

Action
Lateral rotation of the humerus *(It also stablises the shoulder joint)*

Nerve supply
Suprascapular nerve (C5, 6)

Blood supply
Suprascapular artery and the scapular circumflex artery

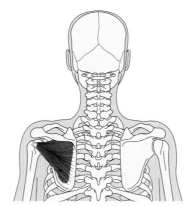

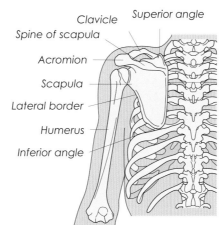

Clavicle
Superior angle
Spine of scapula
Acromion
Scapula
Lateral border
Humerus
Inferior angle

Additional Notes

The shoulder and hip joints are classified as ball-and-socket variations of synovial joints. The shoulder joint has acquired a greater range of mobility compared to the hip.
This mobility has been achieved at the expense of stability, which at the hip is supplied by the shape of the bones and the position of their ligaments.
At the shoulder, stability is provided by deep muscles called *rotator cuff* muscles and the infraspinatus belongs to this group. These muscles encircle the shoulder joint and include the supraspinatus, subscapularis and teres minor.

Possible signs of weakness

The back of the hand may face forwards when the arm is relaxed at the side.
The muscle can be felt if the arm is rotated laterally against a resistance with the arm held at the side of the body. This is done with the arm flexed at the elbow and pushing against the examiner's hand.

Synergists
Deltoid
Supraspinatus
Teres minor

Antagonists
Latisimus dorsi
Pectoralis major
Teres major

Internal obliques

(internal – inside; *oblique* – diagonal to the midline)

Position
They lie under the external obliques

Origin
From the iliac crest and inguinal ligament *(in groin)* and lumbar fascia

Insertion
Into the lower four ribs, pubic bone and linea alba

Action
Compression of the abdomen (see additional notes, right)
Contraction of one side causes lateral flexion of the vertebral column

Nerve supply
Intercostal nerves (T7-12), iliohypogastric and ilioinguinal nerves

Blood supply
Intercostal, subcostal, superior and inferior epigastric arteries

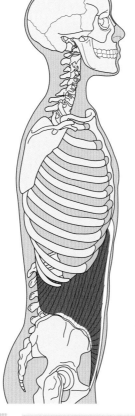
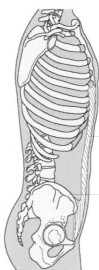

Abdominal aponeurosis

Anterior iliac crest

Additional Notes

The fibres of the muscle run upward and medially in the opposite direction to those of the external obliques. The linea alba is an aponeurosis formed by the fibres of the left and right abdominal muscles. The *umbilicus* is the scar that is left after sectioning of the umbilical cord at birth.

The *lumbar fascia* provides attachment for several other muscles in this area. Contraction is also apparent during defecation, vomiting, urination and childbirth.

Possible signs of weakness

The shoulder may rotate forwards. The trunk may lean towards the weaker side, and, if there is a bilateral weakness, lordosis of the spine may occur.

Synergists
External obliques
Rectus abdominis

Antagonists
Gluteus medius
Gluteus minimus
Opposite obliques

Latissimus dorsi

(latissimus – widest; latus – broad; dorsum – back)

Position
It runs across the back between the pelvis and the humerus

Origin
From the iliac crest, sacrum, lumbar vertebrae and the lower six thoracic vertebrae

Insertion
Into the upper humerus *(the intertubercular groove between the tubercles)*

Action
Medial rotation, adduction and extension of the arm
Helps to pull the arm back, down and inwards, as in throwing

Nerve supply
Thoracodorsal nerve (C6, 7, 8)

Blood supply
Thoracodorsal artery

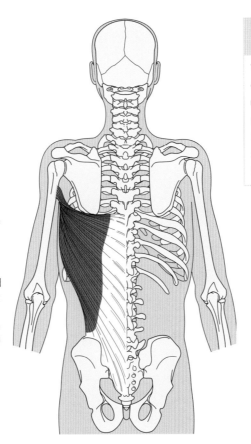

Additional Notes

When throwing an object, the muscle contracts and a distinctive ridge is seen running on the side of the trunk from the pelvic region to the arm pit *(axilla)*.
If a hand is placed on the muscle, it can be seen to contract when coughing. Therefore, it may have some minor role in expiration.

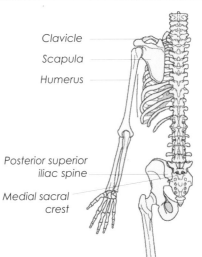

Clavicle
Scapula
Humerus
Posterior superior iliac spine
Medial sacral crest

Possible signs of weakness

The palm may turn to face forwards when the arm is relaxed at the side. The muscle can be felt contracting if the patient coughs while the muscle is held between the finger and thumb at the posterior axillary fold.

Synergists
Pectoralis major
Rhomboids
Teres major

Antagonists
Deltoids
Serratus anterior
Teres minor
Trapezius

Levator scapulae

(levator – raises; scapulae – the scapula)

Position
It runs from the backbone to the scapula

Origin
From the first four cervical vertebrae *(their transverse processes)*

Insertion
Into the upper corner *(superior angle)* of the scapula, nearest the spine and into the upper part of its medial *(vertebral)* border

Action
It raises (elevates) the scapula

Nerve supply
Cervical nerve (C3, 4) and dorsal scapular nerve (C5)

Blood supply
Transverse cervical artery

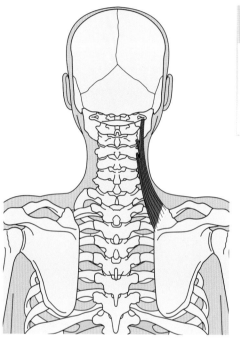

Additional Notes
The muscle forms a prominent part of the fleshy area in the posterior neck. Weakness may also result in reduced mobility of the scapula.

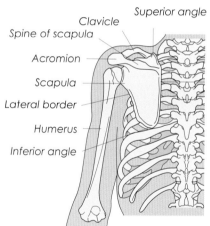

Superior angle
Clavicle
Spine of scapula
Acromion
Scapula
Lateral border
Humerus
Inferior angle

Possible signs of weakness
The scapula may turn so that its inferior angle is rotated outwards. If one is weak, the head may tilt away from that side. If both are weak, the head may tilt forwards.

Synergists
Rhomboids
Trapezius

Antagonists
Neck flexor muscles
Serratus anterior

Pectoralis major

(pectoris – the breast; major – greater)

Position
A large muscle covering the anterior thorax

Origin
From the clavicle *(anterior surface of the inner two thirds)*, sternum *(anterior surface)* and upper six ribs *(from the costal cartilages)*

Insertion
Into the upper humerus *(deltoid tuberosity and bicipital groove)*

Action
Flexion, adduction and medial rotation of the arm at the shoulder

Nerve supply
Lateral pectoral nerve (C5, 6, 7) and medial pectoral nerve (C8, T1)

Blood supply
Pectoral branch of thoracoacromial artery and the internal mammary artery

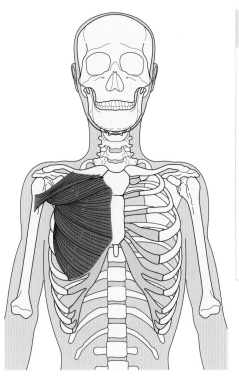

Additional Notes

The muscle forms the anterior wall of the axilla and is partly covered by the deltoid in this area.

When working the muscle it is usually possible to see a distinction between the part of the muscle that originates from the clavicle and that which originates from the sternum and ribs.

The upper *(clavicular)* fibres are involved in flexion of the arm at the shoulder while the lower *(sternocostal)* fibres are used in extension. The latter contraction is more obvious if the arm is extended a resistance.

Manubrium

Clavicle

Body of sternum

Possible signs of weakness

The shoulder may move backwards and the palm may face forwards when the arms are relaxed at the side. There may be difficulty in moving the arm across the chest.
The muscle can be felt if the arm is abducted against a resistance.

Synergists
Biceps
Deltoid
Subscapularis
Teres major

Antagonists
Infraspinatus
Latissimus dorsi
Rhomboids
Teres minor

Pectoralis minor

(pectoris – the breast; minor – lesser)

Position
A small triangular muscle on the anterior thorax (underneath the pectoralis major)

Origin
From the third, fourth and fifth ribs

Insertion
Into the scapula *(coracoid process)*

Action
Anterior rotation of shoulder (as in reaching forward)

Nerve supply
Medial pectoral nerve

Blood supply
Lateral thoracic artery

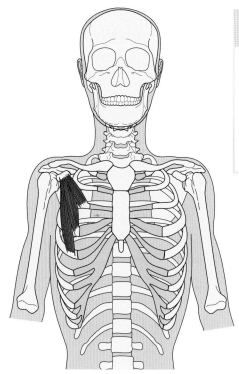

Additional Notes

Some authorities claim that it aids in raising the ribs during inspiration.
When the arms are raised above the head, it may be possible to see the muscle bulging just below the edge of the pectoralis major.

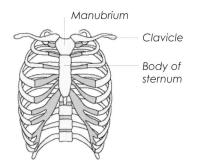

Manubrium
Clavicle
Body of sternum

Possible signs of weakness

The shoulder may move backwards.

Synergists
Pectoralis major
Serratus anterior

Antagonists
Levator scapulae
Rhomboids
Trapezius

Peroneal muscles

(perone – fibula; brevis – short; longus – long)

Position
A pair of muscles on the lateral side of the lower leg; peroneus brevis and peroneus longus

Origin
The lateral aspect of the shaft of the fibula:
• *P. brevis* – from the lower two-thirds
• *P. longus* – from the upper two-thirds

Insertion
P. brevis – into the fifth metatarsal
P. longus – into the medial cuneiform and first metatarsal

Action
Plantar flexion of the ankle and eversion of the foot

Nerve supply
Superficial peroneal nerve (L4, 5; S1)

Blood supply
Branches of the peroneal artery

Possible signs of weakness

Inversion of the foot and inability to evert the foot. More generally, the ankle may be weak with a tendency for the foot to roll outwards. The muscles are often sprained when 'going over' on the ankle.
If the foot is everted against a resistance, the tendon can be felt behind the lower end of the fibula.

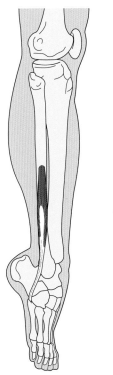

Peroneus brevis *Peroneus longus*

Additional Notes

Even though the muscles are on the lateral aspect of the fibula, they are evertors of the foot. This is mainly due to the insertion of the peroneus longus, whose tendon passes behind the lateral malleolus and across the sole of the foot to the medial side. This muscle also supports the transverse arch of the foot.
There is a third muscle in this group; the peroneus tertius *(tertius – third)*.
However, this is not always present and is likely to be part of the extensor digitorum brevis.

Synergists
Gastrocnemius
Soleus
Each other

Antagonists
Tibialis anterior
Tibialis posterior

37

Piriformis

Position
On the posterior surface of the pelvis, closely associated with the gluteal muscles

Origin
From the scarum *(second, third and fourth segments on their anterior surfaces)*

Insertion
Head of femur *(superior surface of the greater trochanter)*

Action
Lateral rotation and abduction of the thigh

Nerve supply
Sacral nerves (S1, 2)

Blood supply
Superior gluteal and inferior gluteal arteries

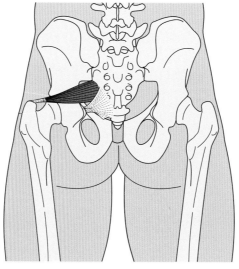

Additional Notes

The superior gluteal artery and superior gluteal nerve pass above it while the sciatic, inferior gluteal and posterior cutaneous nerves of the thigh pass below it.

The muscle often surrounds the sciatic nerve, and, if it becomes over-tense, pain can result in the hip, thigh and down the back of the leg – typical symptoms of sciatica.

It probably holds the head of the femur in the hip socket *(acetabulum)*.

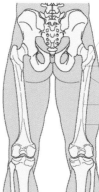

Greater trochanter (femur)

Lesser trochanter

Gluteal tuberosity (femur)

Linea aspera (femur)

Femur

Possible signs of weakness

There may be medial rotation of the thigh and/or signs of knock knees. It may be difficult fo rotate the leg laterally. There may be pronation of the foot.

Synergists
Biceps femoris
Gluteus maximus
Sartorius

Antagonists
Adductors of the thigh
Gluteus medius

Pronator teres

(pronation – turning the palm down; teres – long and round)

Position
Lies at an angle across the anterior forearm

Origin
From the distal end of the humerus *(medial epicondyle)*

Insertion
Into the radius, half-way down the lateral side

Action
Pronates the forearm (turns the palm down) and is involved in flexion at the elbow

Nerve supply
Median nerve (C6, 7)

Blood supply
Branches of the ulnar and radial arteries

Additional Notes

If there is damage to the radial and musculocutaneous nerves, the elbow could still be flexed using this muscle. Its insertion is underneath the extensor carpi radialis longus.

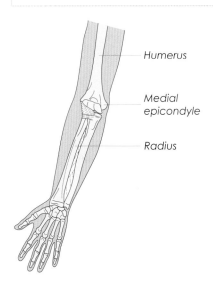

Humerus

Medial epicondyle

Radius

Possible signs of weakness

The palm may rotate forwards independently of the humerus. The muscle can be felt if the patient resists an attempt to supinate the forearm with the arm flexed to 90 degrees at the elbow.

Synergists
Pronator quadratus

Antagonists
Biceps

Psoas

Position
It runs between the lower back and the thigh

Origin
From the twelfth thoracic and all the lumbar vertebrae *(attached to the transverse processes)*

Insertion
Into the head of the femur *(lesser trochanter)*

Action
Flexion and lateral rotation of the thigh

Nerve supply
Lumbar nerves (L2, 3)

Blood supply
Branches of the medial femoral circumflex artery

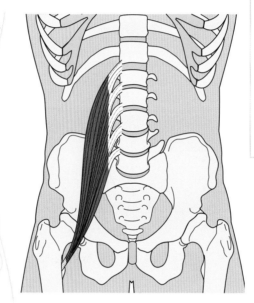

Additional Notes

Together with the iliacus, it is the main flexor of the thigh.
The two muscles are often referred to as the *iliopsoas*.
When lying on the back, they are used to raise the body into a sitting position. To work just the abdominal muscles, sit-ups should not be performed to the vertical position.

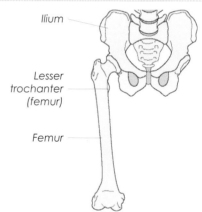

Ilium

Lesser trochanter (femur)

Femur

Possible signs of weakness

May cause posterior rotation of the pelvis.

Synergists
Adductor muscles
Iliacus
Rectus femoris
Sartorius

Antagonists
Gluteus maximus
Gracilis
Hamstrings

Quadratus lumborum

(quadratum – four sided; *lumborum* – lumbar region)*

Position
A rectangular muscle on each side of the lumbar region of the backbone

Origin
From the upper edge of the iliac crest

Insertion
Into the twelfth rib and the first four lumbar vertebrae *(transverse processes)*

Action
Lateral flexion of the vertebral column (towards the muscle that is contracting)

Nerve supply
Intercostal nerve (T12) and lumbar nerve (L1, 2, 3, 4)

Blood supply
Subcostal and lumbar arteries

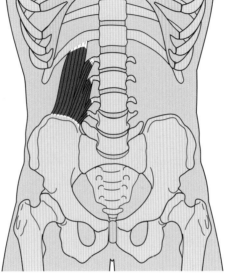

Additional Notes

Part of the lateral arcuate ligament of the diaphragm crosses its anterior surface.

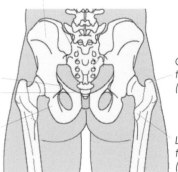

Ilium

Spine of ischium
Body of pubis

Ischial tuberosity

Greater trochanter (femur)

Lesser trochanter (femur)

Possible signs of weakness

The pelvis may twist and the lumbar spine may bend away from the weaker side.

Synergists
External obliques
Internal obliques
Psoas

Antagonists
The opposite quadratus muscle

Quadriceps femoris

(quadriceps – four heads of origin; *femoris* – of the femur)

Position
A group of four muscles covering the anterior thigh

Origin
From the ilium and the shaft of the femur (see additional notes, right)

Insertion
Into the patella and tibia (see additional notes, right)

Action
Flexion at the hip and extension at the knee

Nerve supply
Femoral nerve (L2, 3, 4)

Blood supply
Lateral femoral circumflex, branches of the profunda femoris and descending genicular arteries

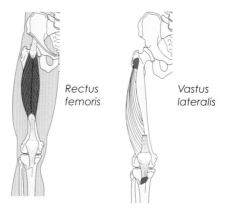

Rectus femoris

Vastus lateralis

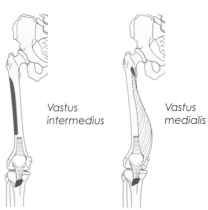

Vastus intermedius

Vastus medialis

Additional Notes

The group consists of the *rectus femoris, vastus lateralis, vastus inter-medius* and *vastus medialis (rectus* – parallel to the midline; *vastus* – large; *lateralis* – lateral; *medialis* – medial; *intermedius* – middle).

The rectus femoris originates from the iliac spine close to the acetabulum and the three vasti muscles originate from the greater trochanter and linea aspera of the femur.

All four muscles insert into the upper border and sides of the patella, from where the patellar ligament runs to the upper surface of the tibia. This ligament is the tendon of the quadriceps and is used in testing the knee jerk reflex.

Due to its origin, the rectus femoris is involved in flexion of the thigh at the hip.

Possible signs of weakness

Possible hyperextension of the knee and posterior rotation of the pelvis. There may also be medial deviation of the knee.
If the patient extends the knee against a resistance while lying on his/her back, the muscle can be seen and felt quite easily.

Synergists
Psoas
Sartorius
Tensor fasciae latae
Other muscles in the group

Antagonists
Gracilis
Hamstrings

Rectus abdominis

(Rectus – fibres parallel to midline; *abdomino* – belly)

Position
A broad, flat muscle running the length of the abdomen

Origin
From the upper edge of the pubic bones and the joint between them *(pubic symphysis)*

Insertion
From the costal cartilages of ribs 5, 6 and 7 and from the xiphoid process of the sternum

Action
Flexion of the trunk/vertebral column (see additional notes, right)

Nerve supply
Intercostal nerves (T7-11) and subcostal nerve (T12)

Blood supply
Superior epigastric, intercostal, subcostal and inferior epigastric arteries

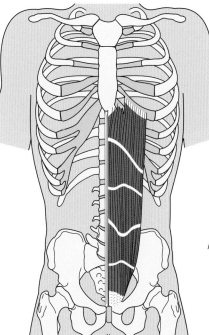

Additional Notes

The muscle usually consists of four distinct sections, particularly in males. It can be contracted to apply tension against the outward pressure of the guts.
Contraction is also apparent during defecation, vomiting, urination and childbirth, and when raising the legs while lying down.

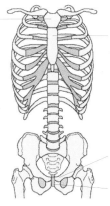

Manubrium

Body of sternum

Pubic crest

Pubic symphis

Possible signs of weakness

There may be a side bend away from the weaker side. Possible lordosis if both sides are weak.

Synergists
External obliques
Internal obliques
Pyramidalis

Antagonists
Gluteus medius
Gluteus minimus
Sacrospinalis

Rhomboids

Position
They lie between the backbone and the scapula *and consist of a major and a minor part*

Origin
From the seventh cervical to the fifth thoracic vertebrae *(spinous processes)*

Insertion
Into the medial border of the scapula *(from the base of the spine of the scapula to its inferior angle)*

Action
Adducts/retracts the scapula (pulls it towards the backbone) and rotates it slightly (so that the glenoid cavity points downwards)

Nerve supply
Dorsal scapular nerve (C5)

Blood supply
Dorsal scapular artery

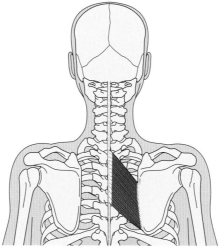

Rhomboid major

Additional Notes

The muscles work with the levator scapulae to retract and rotate the scapula. When they contract, they can be seen to bulge through the trapezius that covers them.

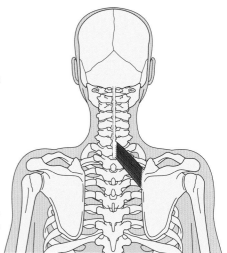

Rhomboid minor

Possible signs of weakness

The scapula may drop and abduct. The shoulder may move forwards and the head may rotate towards the weaker side.
The muscle may be felt if the shoulders are pushed backwards against a resistance.

Synergists
Latissimus dorsi
Levator scapulae
Trapezius

Antagonists
Pectoralis minor
Serratus anterior

44

Sartorius

Position
The longest muscle in the body; runs across the thigh

Origin
From the anterior surface of the ilium (*superior iliac spine*)

Insertion
Crosses the thigh to the head of the tibia (*medial side*)

Action
Flexes the knee, flexes the thigh at the hip and rotates the leg laterally (crossing legs)

Nerve supply
Femoral nerve (L2, 3)

Blood supply
Branches of the profunda femoris artery, saphenous branch of descending genicular artery

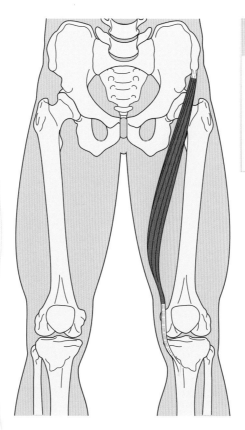

Additional Notes

The muscle is named after the traditional cross-legged position of tailors.

It runs across the thigh from the outside of the pelvis to the medial side of the tibia and because it crosses two joints, it can flex the leg at the thigh and the knee.

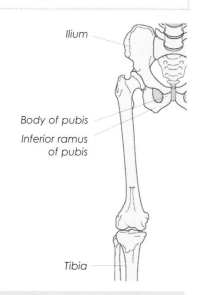

Ilium

Body of pubis

Inferior ramus of pubis

Tibia

Possible signs of weakness

There may be signs of knock knees, and, if both are weak, there may be posterior rotation of the pelvis.

Synergists
Gracilis
Hamstrings
Hip rotators
Psoas

Antagonists
Adductor muscles
Gracilis
Hamstrings

Serratus anterior

(serratus – saw-toothed; anterior – front)

Position
A sheet of muscle running around the sides of the thorax

Origin
From the upper 8 ribs *(as separate strips or digitations)*

Insertion
Into the medial border of the scapula and its anterior *(costal)* surface

Action
Lateral rotation of the scapula when extending the arms or pushing

Nerve supply
Long thoracic nerve (C5, 6, 7)

Blood supply
Lateral thoracic artery and thoracodorsal artery

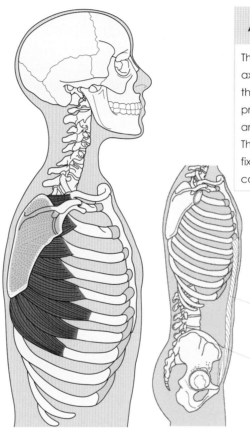

Abdominal aponeurosis

Anterior iliac crest

Additional Notes

The muscle forms the medial wall of the axilla. Its lower digitations insert near to the inferior angle of the scapula and provide great leverage. The upper ones are hidden by the pectoralis major. The serratus anterior also has a role in fixing the position of the scapula if carrying a heavy load.

Possible signs of weakness

There may be difficulty or discomfort when reaching or pushing forwards. Another sign of weakness is 'winging', when the scapula does not lie flat on the ribs. In this condition, the medial border is usually prominent, especially if the arms are raised.

Synergists
Pectoralis minor
Trapezius

Antagonists
Levator scapulae
Latissimus dorsi
Rhomboids
Trapezius

Soleus

Position
Lies underneath the gastrocnemius in the calf

Origin
From the head of the tibia and fibula

Insertion
Into the calcaneus via the Achilles tendon

Action
Plantar flexes the foot

Nerve supply
Tibial nerve (L5, S1, 2)

Blood supply
Posterior tibial artery and branches of the popliteal and peroneal arteries

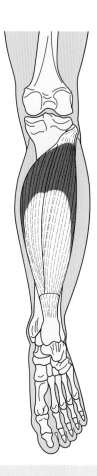

Note: The foot is plantar flexed.

Additional Notes

The soleus has no action on the knee joint because its origin is from the tibia and fibula, unlike the gastrocnemius, which originates from the femur.
It is assumed that the soleus helps to stabilise the ankle, rather than being involved in rapid movement.

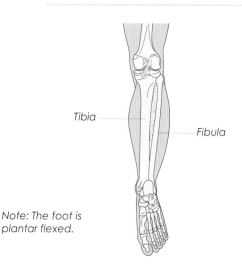

Tibia

Fibula

Possible signs of weakness

There may be difficulty in standing on tip toes.

Synergists
Gastrocnemius
Flexor digitorum longus
Flexor hallucis longus
Peroneal muscles
Tibialis posterior

Antagonists
Tibialis anterior

Splenius capitis

(splenion – a bandage; capitas – of the head)

Position
It lies between the neck and the temporal bone

Origin
From cervical vertebra 7 to thoracic vertebra 3 *(the spinous processes)*

Insertion
Into the mastoid process and superior nuchal line *(lateral third)*

Action
Extension of the neck.
Sideways bending and rotation of the head

Nerve supply
Dorsal rami of spinal nerves (C2, 3, 4)

Blood supply
Muscular branches of the aorta

Additional Notes

Extension of the neck is achieved when both muscles contract. They are also involved in rotation and sideways bending of the head when contracting unilaterally.

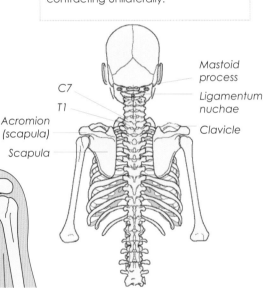

C7
T1
Acromion (scapula)
Scapula
Mastoid process
Ligamentum nuchae
Clavicle

Possible signs of weakness

A bilateral weakness can cause the head to tilt forwards. A unilateral weakness may cause the head to tilt or rotate away from the weaker muscle.

Synergists
Levator scapula
Trapezius

Antagonists
Sternocleidomastoid

Splenius cervicus

(splenion – a bandage; cervicus – of the neck)

Position
Runs between the upper posterior thorax and neck

Origin
From thoracic vertebrae 3-6 *(the spinous processes)*

Insertion
Into cervical vertebrae 1-3 *(the posterior surface of the transverse processes)*

Action
Extension of the neck.
Sideways bending and rotation of the head

Nerve supply
Dorsal rami of spinal nerves (C2, 3, 4)

Blood supply
Muscular branches of the aorta

Additional Notes
Extension of the neck is achieved when both muscles contract. They are also involved in rotation and sideways bending of the head when contracting unilaterally.

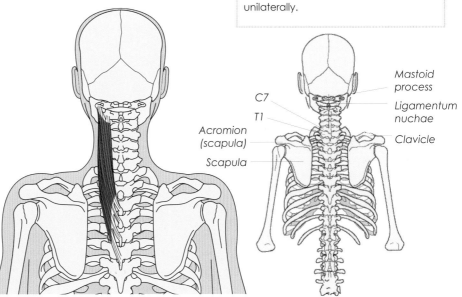

Mastoid process
Ligamentum nuchae
Clavicle
C7
T1
Acromion (scapula)
Scapula

Possible signs of weakness
A bilateral weakness can cause the head to tilt forwards. A unilateral weakness may cause the head to tilt or rotate away from the weaker muscle.

Synergists
Levator scapulae
Splenius capitis
Trapezius

Antagonists
Sternocleidomastoid

Sternocleidomastoid
(sternum – breastbone; *cleido* – clavicle; *mastoid* – mastoid process of temporal bone)

Position
A pair of muscles lying on each side of the neck

Origin
From the sternum *(upper edge of manubrium)* and the clavicle *(upper end of the medial surface)*

Insertion
Into the temporal bone *(mastoid process)*

Action
Bilateral – pull head forwards (nodding)
Unilateral – turn the head to the side (opposite side to contracting muscle)

Nerve supply
Accessory nerve *(X1 cranial)* and cervical nerves *(C2, 3)*

Blood supply
Occipital and superior thyroid arteries

Additional Notes

When the head is fixed using the posterior neck muscles, the sternocleidomastoid can help with inspiration by raising the sternum and upper ribs.

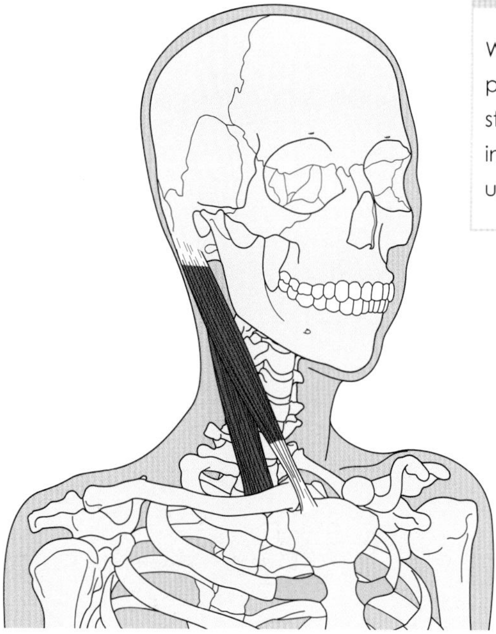

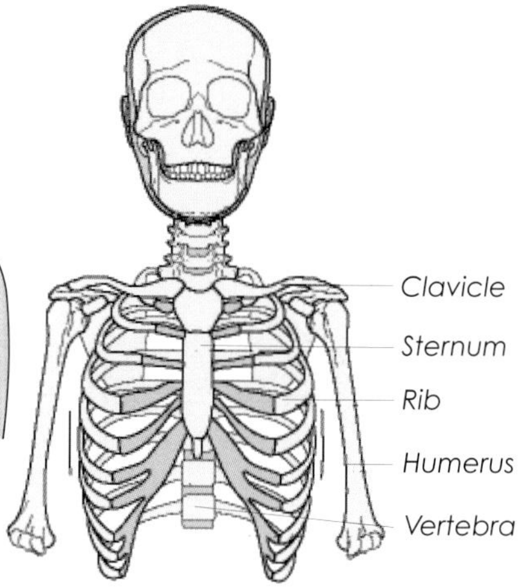

Clavicle
Sternum
Rib
Humerus
Vertebra

Possible signs of weakness

The head may tilt away from the weaker muscle. There may be difficulty in raising the head when lying in a supine position.

Synergists
Scalene muscles
Trapezius

Antagonists
Splenius capitis
Splenius cervicus

Subscapularis

(*sub* – under; *scapularis* – shoulder blade)

Position
It runs from the scapula to the humerus

Origin
From the anterior surface of the scapula *(the subscapular fossa)*

Insertion
Into the head of the humerus *(lesser tubercle)* and the capsule of the shoulder joint

Action
Medial rotation of the arm and stabilisation of the shoulder joint

Nerve supply
Suprascapular nerve (C5, 6, 7)

Blood supply
Branches of the subscapular artery

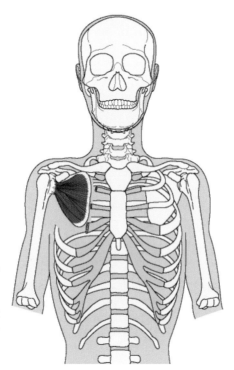

Additional Notes

In order to reduce a dislocation of the shoulder, the muscle must be stretched by gentle, lateral rotation. This is because its tendon of origin lies close to the capsule of the joint.
At the shoulder, stability is provided by deep muscles called the *rotator cuff* muscles and the subscapularis belongs to this group. These muscles encircle the shoulder joint and include the infraspinatus, supraspinatus, and teres minor.

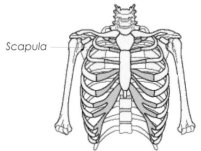

Scapula

Possible signs of weakness

The palm may turn forwards when the arm is held at the side. There may be discomfort and/or difficulty in reaching between the shoulder blades and shoulder mobility may be reduced.

Synergists
Latissimus dorsi
Pectoralis major
Teres minor

Antagonists
Deltoid
Infraspinatus
Teres major

Supraspinatus

(*supra* – above; *spinatus* – of the spine)

Position
Between the scapula and humerus

Origin
Just above the spine of the scapula *(the supraspinous fossa)*

Insertion
Into the head of the humerus *(greater tubercle – superior surface)*

Action
Abduction of arm *(and also stabilises shoulder joint)*

Nerve supply
Suprascapular nerve (C5, 6)

Blood supply
Suprascapular artery

Additional Notes

Its tendon of insertion is attached to the capsule of the shoulder joint and begins to abduct the arm prior to contraction of the deltoid.

At the shoulder, stability is provided by deep muscles called the *rotator cuff* muscles and the supraspinatus belongs to this group. These muscles encircle the shoulder joint and include the infraspinatus, subscapularis and teres minor.

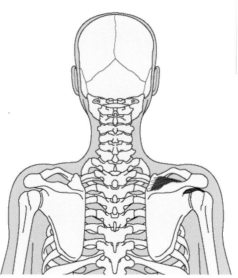

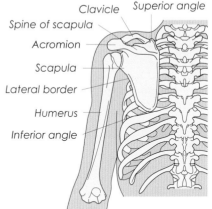

Clavicle
Superior angle
Spine of scapula
Acromion
Scapula
Lateral border
Humerus
Inferior angle

Possible signs of weakness

There may be discomfort and/or difficulty in abducting the arm. The belly of muscle can be felt quite easily if the arm is abducted against a resistance while held against the side of the body.

Synergists
Deltoid
Infraspinatus

Antagonists
Coracobrachialis
Pectoralis major
Teres major
Teres minor

Tensor fasciae latae

(tensor – to tense; fascia – a band; latus – wide)

Position
On outside of thigh at hip

Origin
From the ilium *(anterior iliac crest and superior iliac spine)*

Insertion
Into the iliotibial tract (see additional notes, right)

Action
Flexion and abduction of the thigh at the hips and medial rotation of the leg

Nerve supply
Superior gluteal nerve (L4, 5, S1)

Blood supply
Superior gluteal and lateral femoral circumflex arteries

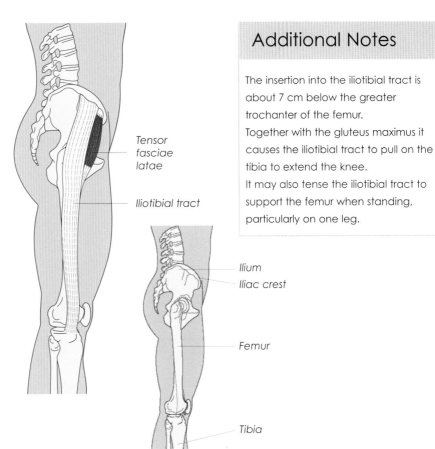

Tensor fasciae latae

Iliotibial tract

Ilium
Iliac crest

Femur

Tibia

Additional Notes

The insertion into the iliotibial tract is about 7 cm below the greater trochanter of the femur.
Together with the gluteus maximus it causes the iliotibial tract to pull on the tibia to extend the knee.
It may also tense the iliotibial tract to support the femur when standing, particularly on one leg.

Possible signs of weakness

Possible instability of the knee and signs of bow legs.
The pelvis may tilt upwards on the weaker side.
Possible difficulty in standing on one leg.
If the patient is lying on his/her back, the muscle can be felt when the thigh is abducted with the leg straight.

Synergists
Gluteus maximus
Gluteus medius
Gluteus minimus

Antagonists
Adductors
Gracilis
Hamstrings
Piriformis

Teres major

(teres – long and round; major – greater)

Position
A thick muscle running from the scapula to the humerus

Origin
From the lower part of the scapula *(lower edge of lateral border and the inferior angle)*

Insertion
Just below the head of the humerus *(on the anterior surface, distal to the lesser tubercle)*

Action
Extends the arm and draws it downwards. It also assists in adduction and medial rotation of the arm

Nerve supply
Lower subscapular nerve (C5, 6)

Blood supply
Thoracodorsal artery

Additional Notes

This muscle is thicker and more round than its partner, the teres minor, and forms part of the posterior axillary wall. The tendon of insertion of the latissimus dorsi passes round it.

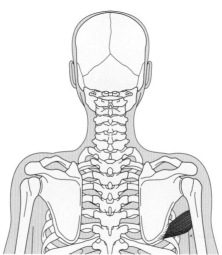

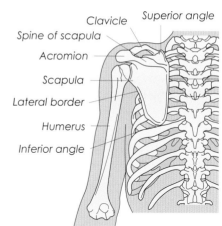

Clavicle
Superior angle
Spine of scapula
Acromion
Scapula
Lateral border
Humerus
Inferior angle

Possible signs of weakness

The palm may turn forwards when the arm is held at the side. There may also be difficulty in reaching backwards. If the arm is adducted against a resistance, the muscle can be felt in the posterior axillary fold.

Synergists
Latissimus dorsi
Subscapularis

Antagonists
Deltoid
Infraspinatus
Supraspinatus
Teres minor

Teres minor

(teres – long and round; minor – lesser)

Position
A thin muscle running between the scapula and humerus

Origin
The scapula *(from the infraspinous fossa near the lateral border)*

Insertion
Into the humerus *(lower facet of greater tubercle)*

Action
Lateral rotation of the arm *(also stabilises the shoulder joint)*

Nerve supply
Axillary nerve *(C5, 6)*

Blood supply
Scapular circumflex artery

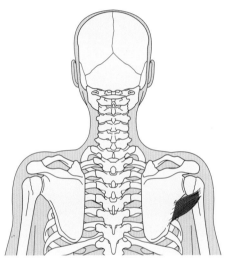

Additional Notes

The teres minor also inserts into the capsule of the shoulder joint.
At the shoulder, stability is provided by deep muscles called *rotator cuff* muscles, and the teres minor belongs to this group. These muscles encircle the shoulder joint and include the infrapsinatus, supraspinatus and subscapularis.

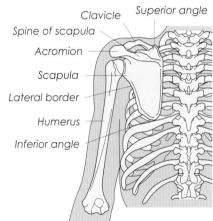

Clavicle
Superior angle
Spine of scapula
Acromion
Scapula
Lateral border
Humerus
Inferior angle

Possible signs of weakness

The palm may turn forwards when the arm is held at the side, and the subject may find difficulty in reaching backwards.

Synergists
Deltoid
Infraspinatus
Subscapularis

Antagonists
Coracobrachialis
Latissimus dorsi
Teres major

Tibialis anterior

(tibialis – of the tibia; anterior – front)

Position
On the lateral side of the lower leg

Origin
From tibia just below the knee *(lateral condyle)*

Insertion
Into the first metatarsal *(of big toe)* and medial cuneiform

Action
Dorsiflexion and inversion of the foot

Nerve supply
Deep peroneal nerve (L4, 5; S1)

Blood supply
Anterior tibial artery

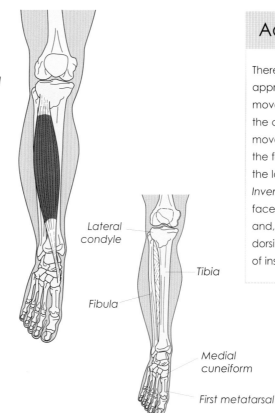

Lateral condyle

Tibia

Fibula

Medial cuneiform

First metatarsal

Additional Notes

There is often confusion regarding the appropriate terminology for movements of the foot at the ankle. In the case of the ankle joint, *dorsiflexion* moves the upper surface *(dorsum)* of the foot towards the anterior surface of the lower leg.

Inversion of the foot causes the sole to face towards the midline of the body, and, when the muscle is used to dorsiflex and invert the foot, its tendon of insertion is very easy to see.

Possible signs of weakness

Possible weakness in the medial longitudinal arch and the foot can roll inwards. There may be pronation or lateral rotation of the ankle.

Synergists
Extensor digitorum longus
Extensor hallucis longus

Antagonists
Gastrocnemius
Soleus
Tibialis posterior

Tibialis posterior

(tibialis – of the tibia; posterior – rear)

Position
Lies deep in the calf

Origin
From the upper shaft of the tibia, the head of the fibula and interosseous membrane

Insertion
Into the lower surface of the second, third and fourth metatarsals, navicular, lateral cuneiform and cuboid

Action
Plantar flexes and inverts foot

Nerve supply
Tibial nerve (L5; S1)

Blood supply
Peroneal and posterior tibial arteries

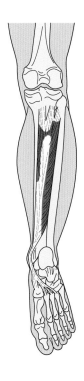

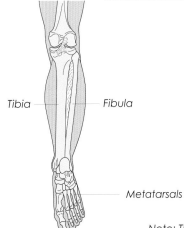

Tibia — Fibula

Metatarsals

Note: The foot is plantar flexed.

Additional Notes

The tendon of insertion passes behind the medial malleolus superficially to the talus and then branches to the lower surface of many of the bones of the foot. This route explains its action in plantar flexion (plantar flexion is in fact extension of the ankle).

Possible signs of weakness

Possible weakness of the medial longitudinal arch and the foot may roll inwards. There may be difficulty and instability when standing on tip toes. If the patient lies in a supine position and tries to invert the plantar flexed foot against a resistance, the tendons can be seen and felt behind the lateral malleolus.

Synergists
Flexor digitorum longus
Flexor hallucis longus

Antagonists
Peroneal muscles
Tibialis anterior

Transversus abdominis

(transversus – fibres run perpendicular to the midline; *abdomino* – belly)

Position
A very deep sheet of muscle running across the abdomen

Origin
From the iliac crest, lower six costal cartilages and the inguinal ligament

Insertion
Into the pubic bone and linea alba

Action
Compresses the abdomen (see additional notes, right)

Nerve supply
Thoracic nerves (T8-12), iliohypogastric and ilioinguinal (L1) nerves

Blood supply
Superior epigastric, intercostal, subcostal, superior and inferior epigastric arteries

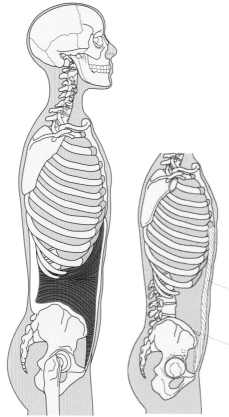

Abdominal aponeurosis

Anterior iliac crest

Additional Notes

The muscle also is known as the transversalis and it has similar attachments to and lies beneath the internal obliques. Many nerves and arteries of the abdominal wall run between these two muscles.
It can be contracted to apply tension against the outward pressure of the guts, and contraction is also apparent during defecation, vomiting, urination and childbirth.

Possible signs of weakness

There may be a lateral bulge in the torso or the spine may curve away from the muscle.

Synergists
External obliques
Internal obliques

Antagonists
Gluteus medius
Gluteus minimus

Trapezius

(trapezoides/trapeza – trapezoid shape; four sides – not parallel)

Position
Covering the shoulders and the back of the neck

Origin
From the occipital bone, *ligamentum nuchae*, seventh cervical and all thoracic vertebrae *(from the spinous process)*

Insertion
Into the clavicle *(posterior side of outer third)* and scapula *(acromion process and spine)*

Action
Elevates clavicle and scapula
Adducts and depresses scapula

Nerve supply
Accessory nerve (X1 cranial) and cervical nerves (C3, 4)

Blood supply
Transverse cervical artery

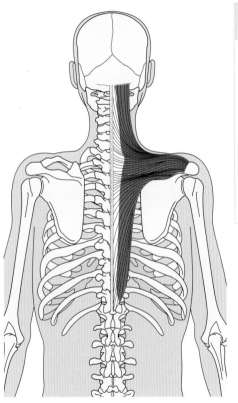

Additional Notes

The muscle is divided into upper, middle and lower portions.
The upper fibres elevate the clavicle and scapula; the middle fibres adduct and elevate the scapula, and the lower fibres pull the scapula downwards.
When all parts of the muscle work together, the shoulders are 'squared' and the scapula is moved towards the midline as in standing to attention.

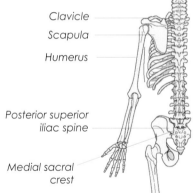

Clavicle
Scapula
Humerus
Posterior superior iliac spine
Medial sacral crest

Possible signs of weakness

The scapula may be elevated and abducted. The head can tilt away from the weaker side. If both sides are weak, the chin may be closer to the chest. The upper fibres can be seen and felt if the patient shrugs the shoulders against a resistance.

Synergists
Levator scapulae
Rhomboids
Serratus anterior

Antagonists
Latissimus dorsi
Pectoralis major
Pectoralis minor

Triceps brachii

(triceps – three heads of origin; brachion – arm)

Position
On the posterior upper arm

Origin
One head from the scapula *(infraglenoid tuberosity)* and two from the humerus *(superior and inferior to the radial groove)*

Insertion
Into the olecranon process of the ulna

Action
Extends the arm

Nerve supply
Radial nerve (C6, 7)

Blood supply
Branches of the brachial, superior ulnar collateral and profunda brachii arteries

Additional Notes

The long head originates from a tubercle on the scapula below the glenoid cavity, the lateral head from the upper humerus below the greater tubercle, and the medial head from the posterior surface of the humerus inferior to the radial groove.

The long head also seems to be involved in adduction of the arm.

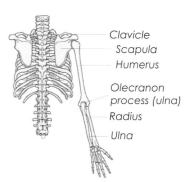

- Clavicle
- Scapula
- Humerus
- Olecranon process (ulna)
- Radius
- Ulna

Possible signs of weakness

The elbow is flexed when the arm is held at the side and the arm may remain bent when raised above the head.

If the forearm is flexed to 90 degrees and then abducted so as to be parallel with the floor, the muscle can be felt if the arm is then extended against a resistance.

Synergists
Anconeus
Shoulder adductors
Shoulder extensors

Antagonists
Biceps
Brachioradialis
Shoulder abductors
Shoulder extensors

How muscles are named

1. Direction of Fibres

rectus	parallel to midline	rectus abdominus
transverse	horizontal/across	transversus abdominis
oblique	at an angle	internal oblique

2. Size

longus	long	flexor hallucis longus
maximus	large	gluteus maximus
vastus	immense	vastus medialis

3. Action of muscles

flexor	bends	flexor carpi radialis
adductor	towards the midline	adductor magnus
levator	lifts	levator scapulae

4. Number of origins/heads

bi	two	biceps
tri	three	triceps
quad	four	quadriceps

5. Location relative to bones/locations of origins and insertions

tibialis anterior	tibia
rectus femoris	femur
sternocleidomastoid	sternum, clavicle and mastoid process

6. Shape

deltoid	triangular
rhomboids	diamond
quadratus	rectangular

Note: The categories above show examples of some terms used in naming muscles and are not exhaustive. Some muscles have names which are combinations of the categories e.g. flexor digitorum longus.

Muscles of the body

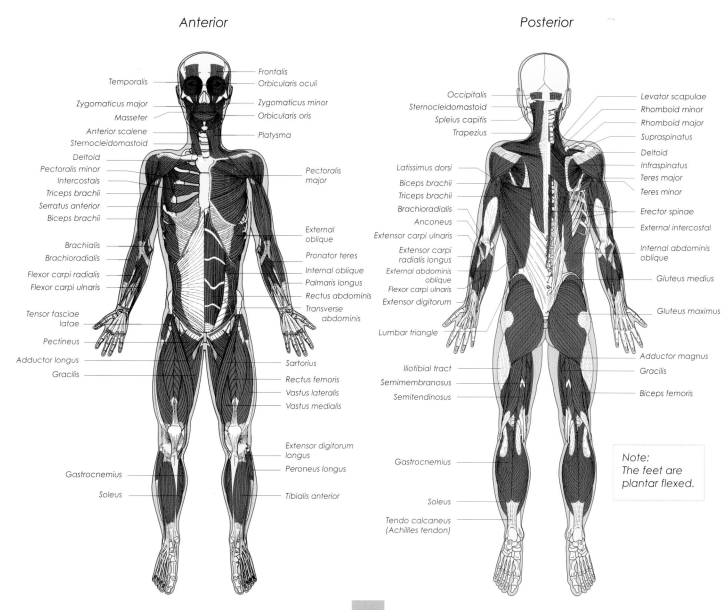

Anterior

- Temporalis
- Zygomaticus major
- Masseter
- Anterior scalene
- Sternocleidomastoid
- Deltoid
- Pectoralis minor
- Intercostals
- Triceps brachii
- Serratus anterior
- Biceps brachii
- Brachialis
- Brachioradialis
- Flexor carpi radialis
- Flexor carpi ulnaris
- Tensor fasciae latae
- Pectineus
- Adductor longus
- Gracilis
- Gastrocnemius
- Soleus

- Frontalis
- Orbicularis oculi
- Zygomaticus minor
- Orbicularis oris
- Platysma
- Pectoralis major
- External oblique
- Pronator teres
- Internal oblique
- Palmaris longus
- Rectus abdominis
- Transverse abdominis
- Sartorius
- Rectus femoris
- Vastus lateralis
- Vastus medialis
- Extensor digitorum longus
- Peroneus longus
- Tibialis anterior

Posterior

- Occipitalis
- Sternocleidomastoid
- Spleius capitis
- Trapezius
- Latissimus dorsi
- Biceps brachii
- Triceps brachii
- Brachioradialis
- Anconeus
- Extensor carpi ulnaris
- Extensor carpi radialis longus
- External abdominis oblique
- Flexor carpi ulnaris
- Extensor digitorum
- Lumbar triangle
- Iliotibial tract
- Semimembranosus
- Semitendinosus
- Gastrocnemius
- Soleus
- Tendo calcaneus (Achilles tendon)

- Levator scapulae
- Rhomboid minor
- Rhomboid major
- Supraspinatus
- Deltoid
- Infraspinatus
- Teres major
- Teres minor
- Erector spinae
- External intercostal
- Internal abdominis oblique
- Gluteus medius
- Gluteus maximus
- Adductor magnus
- Gracilis
- Biceps femoris

Note:
The feet are
plantar flexed.

Bones of the skeleton

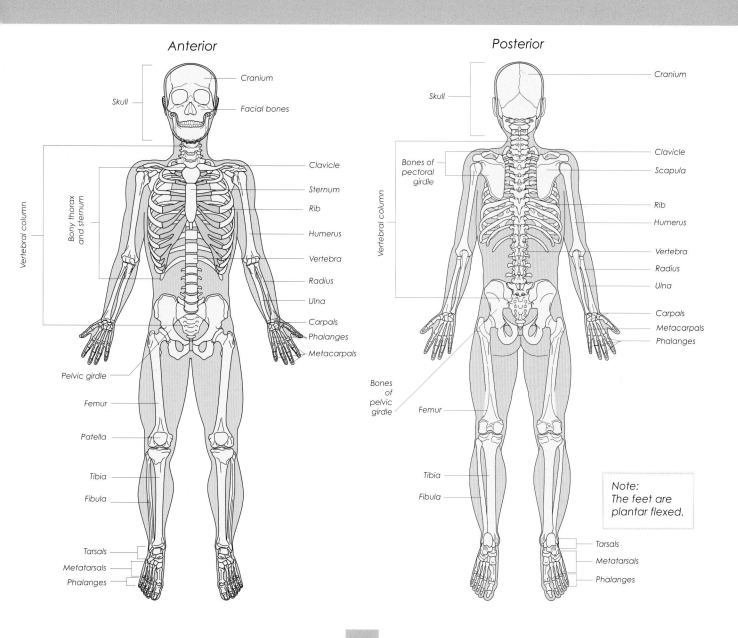

Anterior

Posterior

Skull

Cranium

Facial bones

Vertebral column

Bony thorax and sternum

Clavicle

Sternum

Rib

Humerus

Vertebra

Radius

Ulna

Carpals

Phalanges

Metacarpals

Pelvic girdle

Femur

Patella

Tibia

Fibula

Tarsals

Metatarsals

Phalanges

Skull

Cranium

Bones of pectoral girdle

Vertebral column

Clavicle

Scapula

Rib

Humerus

Vertebra

Radius

Ulna

Carpals

Metacarpals

Phalanges

Bones of pelvic girdle

Femur

Tibia

Fibula

Note:
The feet are plantar flexed.

Tarsals

Metatarsals

Phalanges

Bibliography

- Fox and Pritchard
  Anatomy, Physiology and Pathology for the Massage Therapist
  Corpus Publishing, Lydney, 2001

- J H Green and P H S Silver
  An Introduction to Human Anatomy
  Oxford University Press, Oxford, 1981

- G J Romanes (Editor)
  Cunningham's Textbook of Anatomy
  Oxford University Press, Oxford, 1981

- Gerard J Tortora and Nicholas P Anagnostakos
  Principles of Anatomy and Physiology
  Harper and Row, New York, 1984

- Peter L Williamson and Roger Warwick (Editors)
  Gray's Anatomy
  Churchill Livingstone, Edinburgh, 1980

- Rolf Wirhead
  Athletic Ability and the Anatomy of Motion
  Wolfe Publishing, London, 1994